BAD
UNITED

JUST FOR KICKS

For my teammates Charlie and Mattie,
who believed I could do this

LITTLE TIGER

An imprint of Little Tiger Press Limited
1 Coda Studios, 189 Munster Road, London SW6 6AW

Imported into the EEA by Penguin Random House Ireland,
Morrison Chambers, 32 Nassau Street, Dublin D02 YH68

www.littletiger.co.uk

A paperback original
First published in Great Britain 2024

Text and illustrations copyright © Louise Forshaw, 2024

ISBN: 978-1-78895-666-6

A CIP catalogue record for this book is available from the British Library.

Printed and bound in the UK.

MIX
Paper | Supporting
responsible forestry
FSC® C171272

The Forest Stewardship Council® (FSC®) is a global, not-for-profit organization dedicated to
the promotion of responsible forest management worldwide. FSC defines standards based on
agreed principles for responsible forest stewardship that are supported by environmental,
social, and economic stakeholders. To learn more, visit www.fsc.org

2 4 6 8 10 9 7 5 3 1

LOUISE F☠RSHAW

BAD UNITED
JUST FOR KICKS

LITTLE TIGER
LONDON

CHAPTER ONE

Pick Me!

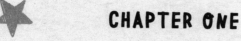

WANTED:

Creatures of any kind who like to kick around a round object.

If you can run/swim/jump/dig/wiggle as fast as lightning – we want YOU to join the MOST EXCITING TEAM YOU'VE EVER SEEN!!

Meet with manager Serena Winmer TODAY if you have what it takes. BAD UNITED needs you!

WARNING:

Risk of being trampled, set on fire, drenched in water/slime/slobber, launched into space, magicked into something entirely different.

☠?⚡☠!!@#☠!?!

CHAPTER TWO

You Ain't
Seen Nothing
Yet

LET'S MEET OUR PLAYERS:

SERENA WINMER

Have fun out there!

Manager, mermaid. Wants you to do your best!

I'm bad to the bone.

BONES

Team captain, skeleton. Often loses her head.

ANNETTE

Catch you soon!

Goalkeeper. Bigger than your average spider.

BOLT

So fast that he's already gone!

TINKERBALL

My moves are magic.

Fairy. Not as sweet as she looks.

REX

The most ROARsome defender.

Big dinosaur. Small arms. Nice smile.

BOLT

I bring the thunder *and* lightning.

Cheetah. You won't see him coming.

CHAPTER THREE

When The Tough Get Going...

22

DRIBBLING:

29

CHAPTER FOUR

Today's
The Day

Nothing was going to stop me from playing my first match with this team.

OK, Bad United, time to show those dragons what we're made of.

Hoof, we'll start with you on the bench.

We all got kitted up …
Hey! That's mine!
Give me that!
Save one for me!
… and THEN we were ready for battle!

UP IN THE COMMENTARY BOX...

Hello football fans! It's amost kick-off time. And here comes the first team!

WE'RE BAD AND WE'RE UNITED! GOOOOO ... BAD UNITED!

43

Let's go to Chuckle who is pitch-side. How are the teams looking down there, Chuckle?

HA HA HA!

HA HA HA

CHAPTER FIVE

A Flying Start?

51

And they didn't get any better.

CHAPTER SIX

There's No 'I' In Team

Well, what a first half that was! The Blazing Dragons are really living up to their name. I can't see how Bad United can come back from that. What do you think Waffle?

Umm, it's not looking good.

If they can just get hold of the ball and score a goal or two, they might claw their way back.

Agreed. If Bones or Rex or Tinkerball or Bolt gets the ball, and they kick the ball, then the ball might go in the goal…

Back in the changing room, Coach tried to lift our spirits.

Come on team. It's not over yet.

Perhaps too much of a spring!

TRIP!

SNAP!

CLICK!

FLASH!

Sorry, Hoof.

STOMP!

The dragons seemed more confident than ever.
It was time to show them what Bad United's made of.

It's never gonna happen, Bones…

68

CHAPTER SEVEN

Never
Say
Never

The second half began and I was ready to support from the sideline.

SQUAAAWK!

You've got this!

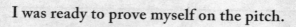

I was ready to prove myself on the pitch.

Errr...

88:34

Time was running out.

81

83

CHAPTER EIGHT

Bring It On